Our Emotions and Behaviour

De____ath

Graves

...by

...ardini

Alex and Lucy were going to school. Then Lucy saw Jack. He was taking Jet for a walk.

Lucy didn't like dogs. She said all dogs were scary. She hid behind Mum.

Mum said that Jet was a nice dog.
She said he only wanted to be friends.
She told Lucy to **calm down** and to
take a deep breath.

Lucy took a deep breath.
She didn't hide behind Mum.

She even gave Jet a little pat.

At school, Tom had a swimming lesson. Miss Button said Tom had to jump into the water.

But Tom did not want to jump into the water. He did not like water going into his ears. He said it made a funny noise.

Miss Button told Tom to **take a deep breath** and to **think calm thoughts.**

Tom took a deep breath.
He jumped into the water.

Miss Button said Tom was **very brave.**

14

Tom was so pleased, he jumped in again...and **again**...and **again!**

At playtime, Dan fell down and cut his knee. He began to cry. Tom told him to calm down and to take a deep breath.

Dan took a **deep breath.**
He stopped crying.

Mr Rose washed Dan's knee and put a bandage on his cut.

He gave him a sticker for **being brave.** Dan was pleased.

In the afternoon, the children put on a play for the whole school.

But Josh did not want to go on the
stage. He did not want everyone
looking at him.

Miss Button told Josh to **take a deep breath** and to **keep calm.**

Josh took **a deep breath.** He went on the stage. Everyone clapped and cheered.

At story time, Miss Button got a book from the bookshelf. A spider landed on her arm. Miss Button did not like spiders.

"Take a deep breath!" said all the children.
Everyone laughed!

Can you tell the story of what happens when Jess has a turn on the big slide?

How do you think Jess felt before she went
on the slide? How did she feel afterwards?

A note about sharing this book

The *Our Emotions and Behaviour* series has been developed to provide a starting point for further discussion on children's feelings and behaviour, both in relation to themselves and to other people.

Take a Deep Breath
This story explores, in a reassuring way, how to overcome fears or nerves by taking a deep breath and staying calm.

The book aims to encourage children to have a developing awareness of their own needs, views and feelings, and to be sensitive to the needs, views and feelings of others.

Storyboard puzzle
The wordless storyboard on pages 26 and 27 provides an opportunity for speaking and listening. Children are encouraged to tell the story illustrated in the panels: Jess is scared of going on the big slide, but she dearly wants to join her friend. She takes a deep breath before having a turn on it and finds to her happy surprise that the slide is great fun.

How to use the book
The book is designed for adults to share with either an individual child, or a group of children, and as a starting point for discussion.

The book also provides visual support and repeated words and phrases to build confidence in children who are starting to read on their own.

Before reading the story
Choose a time to read when you and the children are relaxed and have time to share the story.

Spend time looking at the illustrations and talk about what the book may be about before reading it together.

After reading, talk about the book with the children:

- What was the story about? Have the children ever felt nervous or afraid? What are they afraid of? Talk about coping with and overcoming their fears and who they can turn to for help when they feel afraid.

- Have any of the children been afraid of animals such as dogs or cats, or of insects such as spiders, wasps or bees? Ask them to explore what seems to make some animals and insects scarier than others.

- Find out how many children are afraid of water and learning to swim. Point out that people differ in what scares them and that what frightens one person may not frighten another.

- Talk about the way the characters in the book used the strategy of taking a deep breath and keeping calm. Invite all the children to breathe in and then out slowly. Ask them how they feel after doing this. Point out that taking a deep breath can be very calming.

- Turn to the end of the story where Josh feels afraid and doesn't want to go on stage in front of everyone. Ask the children how Josh felt before his performance. How do they think he felt afterwards? Ask the children if they have had similar experiences. Invite them to share their experiences.

- Look at the storyboard puzzle. Ask the children to talk about Jess's concerns about going on the big slide. How did she feel before she went on the slide? How did she feel afterwards? Again, invite the children to share their experiences of similar occasions. Ask them to tell the others how they overcame their fears.

Suggest that children draw "before" and "after" pictures of times when they have been scared or anxious in the past. In the "before" picture ask them to draw themselves and what they were scared of. In the "after" picture ask them to draw themselves staying calm and overcoming their anxieties.

First published in 2013 by
Franklin Watts
338 Euston Road
London
NW1 3BH

Franklin Watts Australia
Level 17/207 Kent Street
Sydney
NSW 2000

A CIP catalogue record for this book is available
from the British Library.

ISBN 978 1 4451 1625 9

Editor: Jackie Hamley
Designer: Peter Scoulding

Printed in China

Franklin Watts is a division of
Hachette Children's Books,
an Hachette UK company.
www.hachette.co.uk